MICHELINE PARÉ

The Passion of Loving

The Congruent Compassionate Approach™
In Caring for People with Loss of Autonomy

Paulines

© *Paulines*
5610, rue Beaubien Est
Montréal QC H1T 1X5

Translation: Richard R. Cooper

Cover: *Diane Lanteigne*
Layout: *Marcel Provencher*

ISBN: 2-920912-52-6

Dépôt légal :
Bibliothèque nationale du Québec 2005
National Library of Canada 2005

Contents

The Passion of Loving

This book is meant to serve
as *inspiration* to honour both caregiving personnel
and non-professional caregivers;
As a *celebration* of our "stories of love"
about those people suffering from loss of autonomy;
As a *door opening* onto the unconditional love that every
aging human being wishes to receive when he or she is
writing the last chapter of the best-seller of his or her life;
As an *appeal* to everyone in our society to seek
zero tolerance for every kind of abuse or negligence
directed towards suffering and voiceless persons.

Maria and Simone

To care means taking care of the story
of love that belongs to someone else or to us.

Dedication

I am dedicating *The Passion of Loving* especially to two "cutting-edge" women: Maria Labrecque, SP, and Simone Michaud, CSC. To them I owe this charisma, or gift, of compassion towards voiceless seniors that I carry with me as both a privilege and a torment.

Maria's quality of being inspired me with courage and freedom, even when she was suffering from illness at the end of her career as a nurse and administrator. Over a period of fifteen years, I accompanied her on a journey filled with both light and darkness, and my heart was opened in an unexpected way to the suffering and the grandeur of the sick person. Her silent presence taught me to love beyond words, "to the core," that is to love the person in his or her essential being.

It was during this time that the Paré Labrecque Training Centre was initiated.

Simone arrived at the beginning of the Centre as an angel charged with encouraging me in this mission of compassion. As a gentle and generous woman, she shared with us her love for seniors rendered voiceless by illness and her desire to give them a voice.

Just as I was finishing this book, Simone was stricken with illness, but I know that she will continue on the journey with me.

The Transcendent was made manifest through these two extraordinary women who gave to the Centre its Passion of Loving. My friendship and profound gratitude for them are equalled only by their integrity and courage. In leaving, they have left me with the gift of the strength of the wind that guides me into those wide-open spaces where the call of suffering people resounds.

Acknowledgements

To produce a book on compassion requires many people. Thanks go first to the seniors who opened to us the doors of tenderness and the Passion of Loving. But my deep gratitude also goes to:

– our graduates who have chosen to make a difference in the realm of health care: our pride and affection unite them to our "family" forever;

– the members of the Board of Directors for their support and trust. Especially to Mr. Winston Parker, first Vice-President and childhood friend of Maria, who from the beginning of the Centre has not ceased to believe in us. By his generosity, we were able to distribute on May 20th, Maria's birthday, ice cream to the seniors in residences;[1]

– the devoted members of the administrative and teaching staff of the Paré Labrecque Training Centre;

– the healthcare professionals who are involved in caring for each person by surrounding him or her with respect and dignity at every stage of his or her illness;

– the families who are caring for a loved one by guarding his or her comfort and dignity;

– all those who support the mission of the Centre through their financial contributions;

---

[1] May 20th has been proclaimed a Day of Compassion for seniors with loss of autonomy. In our respective locations, let us join in the celebration!

– all those who, with us, welcome this Passion of Loving.

I wish to thank from the bottom of my heart all the dear people who have succeeded in painting with me a picture of life at the centre of suffering. Their support and attention, signs of their compassion in my regard, have truly made them promoters of humanity towards the most deprived of people.

Special thanks go to my mother, Georgette, a loving and courageous woman who accompanied up to the end my father, Léo, who suffered from Alzheimer's disease, as well as thanks to the members of my family for their support to the cause that is so dear to my heart.

Finally, thanks to the team at Éditions Paulines, and especially to Sister Vanda Salvador, FSP, for her welcome and her confidence.

Preface

Dementia is a difficult subject to deal with, all the more when it strikes someone close to you. Often described as sailing into fog and darkness, and navigating through stormy, terrifying seas, dementia leaves sufferers locked in a formless present, deprived of their memories, and heading for uncertain, uncharted horizons.

Some years ago, my own mother was a victim of Alzheimer's disease – the most common form of dementia – and I know first hand the challenges the illness presents not only to sufferers, but also to families and friends, as well as to those whose life's work consists in offering patients comfort, care, and compassion.

So I feel privileged to be writing this preface to Micheline Paré's book *The Congruent Compassionate Approach*, an insightful and moving work that offers hope, guidance, and inspiration to all those affected by the disease, either directly or indirectly. By emphasizing the development of holistic care based on unconditional love and a deep understanding of patients' needs – by reminding us that amid a loss of autonomy dementia sufferers retain their ability to feel – this book defines an original approach and provides deep insights into the nature of love and caregiving.

Although Alzheimer's accounts for approximately 70% of all dementias in Canada, it is only one of 55 other ailments that include Parkinson's, Pick's, and Creutzfeldt-

Jakob's diseases. Common to all these disorders is a gradual and generally permanent decline of mental capacities, with symptoms including losses of memory, judgement, and reasoning. According to the Canadian Psychological Association, 8% of Canadians over the age of 65 suffer from dementia, a proportion that jumps to 37% for those over 85 years of age. Moreover, in 2001, some 364,000 Canadians suffered from the disease, which, with 10,000 casualties every year, is the fourth leading cause of death in our country after cancer, heart disease and stroke.

The origins of dementia are a mystery, and a cure remains elusive for most forms of the disease. However, given the progress of science and medicine, hope is on the horizon. Besides, research demonstrates that patients' quality of life can be considerably improved by offering them the care and support they need.

And offering care, hope, and support to seniors in loss of autonomy has been Micheline Paré's life's work. Inspired by the vision, dedication and mission of her good friend Sister Maria Labrecque, a nurse who administered several health care facilities across Canada, Micheline Paré opened the Paré Labrecque Training Centre in 1994. At the core of the centre's curriculum is a principle known as the Congruent Compassionate Approach, which instils in caregivers a mission to respond with unconditional love and complete dedication to suffering, with a view to creating a providential bond between caregiver and patient.

Seeking to perceive, understand, and ease the fears and anxieties of those suffering from cognitive deficiencies, the Congruent Compassionate Approach is the result of the author's profound meditation and vast experience. I believe she best summarizes this principle when she says:

"Compassion, or the Passion of Loving, is the congruence between a creative thought and compassionate healing. Suffering opens the door to tenderness, but only the Passion of Loving tracks an indefinable orbit for each act of tenderness. A call to limitless love, to love to the very core, finds its source in that passion. This reality demands that we share our passion for caring so as to remain 'missioned.'"

For several years, Micheline Paré has instilled her wisdom to all those who have studied at the Paré Labrecque Training Centre. Now, thanks to this book, that wisdom is available to a wider audience, and I know it will inspire countless other caregivers to see their mission in a new light, and give hope to all those whose loved ones must grapple with cognitive deficiencies.

The Honourable Dan Hays
Speaker of the Senate of Canada

June 28, 2005

Introduction

Our complicated lives require us to balance our needs and responsibilities while dealing with our personal relationships. Sometimes we cannot be where we would like to be or do what we would like to do for those we love. One instance of such a need may well be dealing with the infirmity and decline of those we love. For some this reality is addressed later in life and for some it happens earlier (before the hardening years afford limited protection).

Catherine was her name at birth but Kay thereafter, and our trip to the end of her life as we know it started four years before the "now." Cognitive impairments became clear four years ago, and "what ifs" aside, it was apparent Kay needed others to care for her. She and I were in different countries and thousands of miles distant.

It was obvious that it was a journey others knew well. I took Mom back to her apartment so I could gather needed items; a process repeated many times, and one that was, unfortunately, easier and easier to accomplish as her life grew smaller and smaller as measured in the material wake that follows our lives. I saw in other's eyes: Oh my God, I didn't see it coming and that could be me. I saw fear – not so much of death but of a gradual and rotting decay.

My wife and I are blessed with a loving daughter and son-in-law who live close by to where Mom needed to live. Without them what was hard would have been immeasurably harder. The journey required four years and seven residences (and some hospitalizations). It was a hard trip during which many good people were met, and some not-so-good situations were experienced.

Close to the end of that trip I wrote to unburden myself:

I stepped off the elevator and saw a woman that I forced to become my Mom, unseen for about three months, sitting asleep in a wheelchair with hair undone, mouth agape, and head askew in what I thought would be a painful position. I touched her gently on the shoulder and she roused to semi-consciousness and mumbled about being in pain, "everything hurt, please take the pain away, please let me be dead."

I hugged her and stroked her face and hair. This brought her a little more into my world: enough so she verbalized more about her suffering and how much she hurt. Persistent themes emerged with the worst for me (because it struck too close to home) that the doctor said the pain was bad but he couldn't do anything about it. The helplessness gnawed at me.

I felt guilty because: I was selfish; I hadn't been there enough; I brought her back to my world only to experience pain when her world may have been less painful.

I acknowledged feelings of sadness, frustration, fear, anger, hopelessness, and helplessness. I didn't deal with those feelings. I knew it would take me a lot of time to do that – much more than I had available. By acknowledging my feelings I was able to put them away, in what I hoped would be trustworthy (to stay closed) file drawers. I would know where to find them when I was safe and maybe then I would open them and look. Maybe then.

There are infinite variations on the theme: someone you love needs assistance as they become more helpless and less able to effectively speak for themselves. Sometimes a spouse or child cares for the person for almost the entire journey. Often, however, we need the help of strangers who become the extended family.

I share Kay's end here because I see this as an important book with a simple but powerful set of messages. The book deals with more than rational thought. I don't mean to suggest that the ideas that Micheline advocates do not make sense or are illogical. I suggest one must approach this topic with the heart as well as head for two basic reasons: 1) that is the way most people deal with this issue – with their hearts; and 2) it is the right way to approach it in order to keep our own humanity and honour those who are voiceless and growing more helpless.

Micheline discusses ideas that helped us to help Mom. I took her home to my heart and let her live there while suffering. I used my knowledge of her life and her beliefs to help create a reality for us to share that was better than the one she was experiencing and better than the one that the synthetic morphine could produce.

As Micheline was wise enough to say: "Everything is written in her story and that is still there… Her mind may be trapped in her illness but not her heart and its capacity to feel you. Even if she cannot say so or remember it is you, she feels you."

I did what I could to welcome her into my heart and find the safest place I could for her even though it felt very unsafe for me.

And two interesting and disturbing things happened.

I felt her want to be dead and I felt myself welcome the grace it would afford. At the same time I felt shame and guilt for both welcoming death and for not being more ashamed of having those thoughts. I didn't know how to handle it all and became confused and perhaps even paralysed.

As a psychologist I understand why what happened next happened, but at that moment I wasn't a psychologist and so the something that happened was unexpected.

The last place for Mom was the best that I experienced during the trip. There was heart there and friendliness and even dogs. And those on the staff were open and approachable.

Perhaps it was their characteristics or my experiences with other residents; but regardless of why, I felt compassion for all of those who were brutalized by our journey and the numerous other journeys playing out this day, and every day, at the places where people go to await release. I felt compassion for those whose eyes said: Please don't let this be the way I must go – moaning in a chair and begging kindness from strangers and waiting for sleep – either temporary or permanent. I felt compassion for staff immersed every day in the misery of those growing old, weak, and pained without the solace of meaningful hope for a good recovery, and for medicine that so values life that it treats death as though it is so powerful that its name cannot even be said.

Micheline believes (and teaches) that staff need not see their jobs this way but can and should, instead, see themselves as giving and getting love from their interactions with pain.

This view offers hope that change can come to places that care for moms and dads and everyone else.

I believe that as long as staff come from a culture of scarcity – whether that scarcity is of love, money, or respect – it is inevitable that they will find ways to protect themselves from the suffering they see. That self-protection will be both physical and psychological and will ultimately serve to distance those who serve from those they intend to serve.

Only when those who serve the suffering see themselves as getting something from their participation with those who are in misery, can we expect they will truly be able to approach their work and care for those who are in their charge in more than satisfactory ways.

And for this to happen I believe there needs to be a "makeover" to the system: different training (like the kind advocated in this book); a supportive environment (physically, socially, and culturally) for residents and staff; and changes to a culture that de-values those who are not producing and are infirm.

Those who care for the voiceless must be taught it is their right and duty to have a voice for those who are in their care. Their empathy must be nurtured and not dashed on the rocky shores of professionals protecting turf or unions protecting jobs. These bedside caregivers must champion those in their charge. The system requires all kinds of checks and balances to become more congruent in truly offering compassion and respect to those who cannot demand it because of their circumstances.

Micheline has commented to me:

> "Staff feels helpless at times, but my caregivers [the ones from her school] and many others feel so many rewards as they comfort, help, love, make them feel secure, and accepted. They see the patients responding with trust, they see them smile, they receive a gentle touch from them, etc. This is real care. I experienced that personally with someone I loved and it was very painful at times because of neglect and abuse — of both of us. It was then a torment. But at times of unconditional love — it was the gentleness of a caress felt by both of us. Then it was a privilege."

What you will read about deals with what is beyond our senses (common or otherwise) and deals instead with faith, hope, belief in humanity, and how we can benefit in our dealings with misery, pain, sickness, and hopelessness. It is in some sense irrational to be compassionate to a point of deeply feeling the hurt of those who will never get better. It is right, however, for us as people to do that because we grow personally and help those needing our love and help.

The approach, the topic, and the philosophy transcend reason.

This book is written for healthcare workers who care for voiceless seniors. It is about the process that is almost inevitable as we deal with death, illness, disability, and loss of instrumental and personal autonomy. Counterbalancing the surround of loss, pain, and other negatives are love, respect, intimacy, and faith. It is often hard to reach that point where the spiritual can balance the cold and ever-present realities of failed personal hygiene. This book helps, and since it is such a lonely struggle anything that helps is good.

> The role of "my caregivers" is to care for their [the patients'] past which never leaves them and to have complete respect for their comments. And caregivers should decode and understand this "unknown and unseen" that they hear (that seems not appropriate at times, but still reveals their story) and to receive them as they are and treat them with love and respect. Their past, their message, their words, and their feelings are sacred... no matter how they sound.

Micheline's book is about overcoming fear, avoidance, and despair. It is, for me at least, about feeling compassion for the dying person and being able to move into desperation, understand it, and how not to be afraid of its look, feel, and smell. I tried, and drew strength from being compassionate, and my mother felt it, I believe. My unconditional love – given over and over again – helped me to overcome my fear of the decline and death I saw waiting.

I wanted then and now to believe that I related to her above her pain and as a human being. Transcendent love bridges pain and suffering.

Psychologists have learned that beliefs based on feelings are often more satisfying and resistant to doubt and decay than completely rationally based systems of beliefs. Of course, we can't live our lives wholly on the basis of feelings. Maybe, however, we need to be guided in our experiences with death more on the basis of transcendent love than reason.

Dr. Mark Dimirsky

PART ONE

Definition of the Congruent Compassionate Approach

The Congruent Compassionate Approach is the name I gave to the philosophy and methodology that are practiced in our Centre and that serve as a basis for the relationship between the patient and the caregiver. My dear friend Maria, herself a healthcare professional, was the person with whom I experienced intensely the depth of loving "to the core" during the daily course of her lengthy illness. The painful experience of unconditional love was at the same time one of the most fulfilling experiences I have ever had. When suffering is especially intense, we are faced with the following alternative: either to abandon ourselves to it or to use it as a starting point to create. So that this suffering would not be in vain, but would bear fruit, I decided to establish the Paré Labrecque Training Centre.[2] I wanted seniors who had lost their autonomy, like Maria, Simone, and my father Léo, to be able to receive from the caregivers

---

[2] Incorporated as the *Paré Labrecque Training Centre.*

who worked with them a welcome that was fitting to their unique value. I also wanted the relationship established between the patient and the caregiver to be imprinted with the deepest respect and the greatest competence. This was in order that Alzheimer's disease, as well as other forms of dementia, which is experienced as a "high wall" (Alzhei-murus) could become a "high love" (Alzhei-amor). My wish has already been realized since several hundred graduates of the Centre and practitioners of the Congruent Compassionate Approach have assured me that their strenuous professional lives have also become the location for new stories of love.

In order to explain the philosophy behind this approach, it is first necessary to define the keywords that illustrate the methodology of caregiving:

Mission: A call that comes from without and to which one responds with the feeling of having been supplied with a personal charisma, or gift, for living out the patient/caregiver relationships with those who are suffering.

Compassion: To know what compassion is, is to be tormented by the torment of another, that is, to care for the sufferer with an unconditional love that ensures respect and dignity to the patient at every stage of the illness.

Congruence: This word was chosen to emphasize the importance of living the mission of compassion with authenticity through concrete acts of love that nourish the providential relationship between the patient and the caregiver. From word to act!

It should be noted that this approach does not target only seniors, but every person, universally, who is in need of assistance.

In this publication, every section is followed by a blank space that has been set aside for your use.

You can note down there the fruits of your labours, your discoveries, your hopes, and even your troubles.

Letting your heart speak as you employ pen or brush is a way of growing and healing.

I am offering this work to you with the aim of journeying along with you.

Together, we will be able to "make a difference" in the area of health care.

These written notes will also form a concrete index of deepening experience and, especially, become a means of finding life solutions. Used as personal reflections or ways of sharing, these notes can be a guiding light for you.

Synthesis of my experience

The idea of writing this book and the desire to do it have been with me for many years. I have greatly appreciated the moments of calm when I was able to sit beside a lake or hike in the Rockies while my thoughts blended with the landscape, even to its horizon. My story emerges from such conversations with the universe, which receives all the throbbings of my heart: those of my Passion of Loving in all its boldness as much as in its weak strivings to survive.

These exchangesr, whether in words or in silence, brought me a new vision of my own inner centre even if, at times, I had the impression of propelling everything into the realm of mystery. The goings and comings of these interior movements created a new depth that transformed itself into energy. This power, like fire, renewed my commitment to join with others in their sufferings, which were often greater than mine.

As a non-professional caregiver in a context in which family and friends were intimately connected with sick people, I found that I was "tormented" by the latter's right to dignity and respect. In a medical world in which these values often seem to be absent, I kept insisting that justice be done to every suffering person as a human being at every stage of his or her illness. My constant journeying along with people who were in some ways very diminished enabled me to determine that an atmosphere favourable to the expression of unconditional love stimulated my energies and impelled me to create a place where patient and caregiver could experience harmonious, congruent encounters that would promote the well- being of the person being helped.

On the other hand, like a great many caregivers, whether professional or not, I experienced periods of exhaustion, rebellion, and profound sadness for lack of a place where care was given in a just and healthful way. I realized that, unfortunately, negligence in nursing care and abuse of patients or the elderly exist in many places.

Confronted with these two incompatible worlds, care-givers who believe in life and who are committed to "making a difference" in the art of caregiving are our hope for today and tomorrow. They require our support and gratitude. Through their courage and determination to practise their profession "against the grain," they are providing an inestimable healing balm for patients in painful situations. These patients, no matter what the depth of their silence or the gravity of their condition, are able to "feel" the quality of the way we approach them "here and now" through our daily actions. When illness prevents residents in homes or patients in hospitals from telling us their stories and their sorrows, those who are accompanying them have to decode their silence. Welcoming and understanding are ways of healing. The Congruent Compassionate Approach therefore takes on the character of a journey along the way of the sacred.

At the time when I was very much involved in my career, the task of accompanying a suffering person who was very dear to me plunged me into feelings of loss in the midst of huge challenges. Thanks to the support of loyal friends, I succeeded in remaining connected to life and to the universal. The experience of being welcomed and understood is one of existence's most beautiful gifts. Its healing power clothed my heart again with courage and tenderness. It also sent me "to mission" at the bedside of seniors who have lost their autonomy. I wanted to calm their fears and relieve their solitude. What had seemed to me one of the greatest sufferings in the world had become a place for the incarnation of tenderness. More than anything else, I discovered and felt how patient and caregiver can meet on these "least frequented routes" where giving and receiving are experienced together.

A limpid sound rises amidst the silence; a trail of pure colour drifts through the glass; a light glows for a moment in the depths of the eyes I love... Three things, tiny, fugitive: a song, a sunbeam, a glance... So, at first, I thought they had entered into me in order to remain there and be lost in me. On the contrary, they took possession of me, and bore me away...[3]

By giving me more inner space, my journeying with a dear one diminished by illness opened for me unexpected horizons of communion. Beyond words and actions, a mission of compassion took root in me from the beginning of this encounter.

My mission has now become integrated with the efforts of all the men and women who are working together for a better humanity. In search of its own grandeur, it has been projected into the grandeur of this universal task. This is the great challenge of that "high love" (Alzh-amor) that beyond time and space continues to say that love never stops creating. If one of humanity's missions is to launch human beings into space, would it not be even more wonderful to launch the infinity of space, time, and love into humanity?

The thousands of hours spent in extended-care centres with people suffering from Alzheimer's and other forms of dementia are the origin of the Congruent Compassionate Approach.

This book is intended to open the doors of compassion in all caregivers. From this, I hope that everyone who is

---

[3] Pierre Teilhard de Chardin, *Hymn of the Universe*, trans. Simon Bartholomew (New York and Evanston: Harper & Row, 1965), p. 79.

suffering will feel accepted and enveloped by unconditional love.

It may be that you are reading this book because you are:
 – the son or daughter of someone with Alzheimer's;
 – the friend of someone who has had multiple strokes;
 – someone who has witnessed a patient being accompanied by his or her family;
 – someone who supports compassionate caregivers;
 – someone looking for answers about the quality of care;
 – someone who has been hurt by seeing unresolved situations of abuse suffered by patients incapable of expressing their suffering;
 – someone who has been privileged to receive from a patient of diminished capacities signs of love and gratitude for your efforts.

May this volume bring you comfort, hope, and the love you need.

Components of the Congruent Compassionate Approach

Focusing on the needs of those who are suffering, caregivers seek to respond to the following questions:
What are the types of care that can contribute most to the comfort of the patient? What resources are available for the caregiver who wants to perform compassionate actions?
It would no doubt be interesting to survey the whole world, collecting the research and discoveries of all times

concerning this kind of relationship, and to produce, if possible, a how-to manual. Every problem would find its solution there, every question its answer, every passion its way of being shared. Yet, the relationship between patient and caregiver remains an unfinished symphony. It is impossible to categorize it or to fix it in place. How could we encapsulate in a definition, a task, a stage in a process, without making it into something mechanical?

The role this relationship plays is to call us to be "specialists in humanity." Two human beings confined in a precise location live out a patient/caregiver relationship within the dimension of humanity. Their acts of compassion contribute to the well-being of a society whose borders are thus enlarged in a great, universal movement. Every act of unconditional love and every contribution to the well-being or better quality of life of someone is linked to the advancement of the universe. Thus, within the patient/caregiver's relationship, we are creators and promoters of humanity. Moreover, this universal dimension of humanity experienced within the caregiving context is incarnated and becomes active in everything that is both verbal and non-verbal, that is, within all relational acts.

The relation between patient and caregiver is a complex one. It is difficult to define in a completely satisfying way. First, it emerges from the encounter between someone who has lost his or her health and an autonomous person who is moved by the desire to bring relief. These two people, who do not necessarily share the same values, cultural background, or religion, are going to establish a unique relationship.

The knowledge and techniques employed in freely given care accompany the holistic expression of human actions that ensure respect and dignity at every stage of the individual's illness.

The rapport felt between patient and caregiver becomes a place where two stories, two beings in time and space, meet. It is therefore essential that the caregiver enter with reverence into the space of the person being cared for. Approaching the resident of a home is like entering a foreign country where a unique history filled with humanity and, indeed, the sacred has unfolded. Caregivers accept and understand that they themselves are potentially residents there.

The relationship that unites patient and caregiver is also a place of creative activity. Far from enclosing us in a dossier, a care plan, and mechanical procedures, this encounter between two unique beings is strongly dynamic. The caregiver enters a world of discovery where knowledge and emotional intelligence operate together. Listening and analysis of the state of the patients become for the persons accompanying them sources for the development of thought, feeling, and action.

According to the Congruent Compassionate Approach, the art of caregiving is based on a personal initiative undertaken by caregivers: they choose to commit themselves to a benevolent relationship founded upon respect for everyone. Their manner of living and serving reveals their will to compassion. They move from words to acts and commit themselves to becoming promoters of humanity.

To maintain this benevolent relationship, caregivers have to take the time to discover the richness of their own identity and their capacity for being happy.

To symbolize the unconditional love that lies at the core of the Congruent Compassionate Approach, a flower with five petals is offered to caregivers as a means of exploration, reflection, and personal growth.

Each petal corresponds to a relation:
1. the relation to the universe,
2. the relation to the other,
3. the relation to oneself,
4. the relation to the Transcendent,
5. the relation to life.

These relations are experienced interdependently according to the rhythm of our experiences, and they lead us to the actualization of our potential. The ability to discover, to heal, and to realize ourselves is within our grasp. The expression of our calling relies upon all the paths where respect and dignity for one's self and for those who are most deprived can be found.

Path for exploration:

Am I a creator and promoter of humanity? If so, how?

1. *The relation to the universe*

To open oneself to the Congruent Compassionate Approach is to extend one's arms across the width of the universe. The heart that lifts them up has no bounds.

> Man has the right to be anxious about his fate so long as he feels himself to be lost and lonely in the midst of created things. But let him discover that his fate is bound up with the fate of nature itself, and immediately, joyously, he will begin again his forward march.[4]

It can happen that along the way we run headlong into the inexplicable and the unbearable. The various elements of nature are thus accompanying our quest for meaning.

Over the course of the years, my brief periods of rest in nature have become necessary for my paths of compassion. For example, dawn is a very dear friend who is familiar with all the times and seasons, both peaceful and turbulent, of my feelings. She helps me day-by-day live compassion towards others and towards myself. Although this journey is my own, it can suggest to you how you can identify your journey.

Nature, the element of the cosmos, is always there to receive us, whatever the tale of our adventures may be. She is always ready to give us our dose of inspiration, quiet, or courage. Her heart and arms are full of resources to supply us with sustenance and beauty. When challenges seem to

---

[4] Pierre Teilhard de Chardin, *Hymn of the Universe*, p. 107.

be beyond our strength, we then realize that our encounter with Nature was all too brief!

It is wise to take time to empty ourselves in order to better fill ourselves again.

In every age, the scientists, theologians, artists, writers, poets, philosophers, and pilgrims that we are have sought for meaning, direction, and a way to nurture our immediate need to realize ourselves.

In the heat of battle, we try to find a total, final answer to all our quests for love, meaning, and happiness.

At both home and work, we try to find harmony and a balance between giving and receiving. We are successful in this pursuit if we know how to set aside periods of rest between the starting point and the arrival point.

We can use these periods of rest to study our road map. They can lead us into contact with unsuspected elements of life.

Our passion for life and, occasionally, our efforts to take flight require time for retreat and analysis. Out of that time, comes a new perspective, which is our connectedness with immensity, the unknown, complexity, and beauty. And this connectedness encourages, nourishes, and, indeed, calls us to growth. Our impression of being propelled at top speed into the void, along with the poignant sensation of distance, finally transforms itself into a group of clear indicators. Our periods of rest bring us to a new vision of our own inner centre and of our mission.

The universe is turned into a special place for care-givers.

Path for exploration:

What is my relation to the universe? I am going to write it down.

2. *The relation to the other*

At the heart of this great cosmos, human life takes shape and becomes clear in a vast range of faces and personalities. This mass of individuals attempts to find a way to the actualization of their potential and the realization of their dreams.

From birth to the last breath of life, every person expresses his or her ordinary being in a long story punctuated by boldness and challenges of all kinds.

There are as many stories as there are people, and that has been so since the beginning. Our planet seethes with all the efforts, gropings, and achievements of each and all. It offers itself as a place of meeting between the similarities and differences at the heart of humanity. This human community so rich in talents bears an immense responsibility: that of sharing and creating a world in which everyone has the right to determine his or her existence.

The uniqueness of each individual is closely linked to that of the others in order to form a community. Through concentric circles, the family expands out to join the network of friends and colleagues at work; and it assumes the role of builder of humanity.

However humble our individual stories may be in the great seething mass of humanity, they nonetheless form part of the writing of the history of a people. It is the responsibility of each of us to create a soul for it.

Those of us who choose to accompany a suffering fellow being are committing ourselves to surrounding with compassionate care that pilgrim who has become tired, injured, and alone.

Well beyond the material aspect of work, the profession of caregiving becomes a mission to welcome and surround in a holistic manner a person weakened by illness or age. The chapters of his or her life are unknown in their depths. It is up to us to welcome this day's injury and to envelope it in unconditional love. Don't we all need to be loved unconditionally?

To care means taking care of the story of love that belongs to someone else or to us. It is to desire that the quality of our caregiving should give birth to a patient/caregiver relationship of the most beneficial kind.

The relation to the other is a relationship to be discovered!

Path for exploration:

How would I define my relationship to the other? I am going to select various people and describe my relationship with each of them.

(additional space on verso)

Suffering opens the door to tenderness,
but only the passion of loving
tracks an indefinable
orbit for each act of tenderness.

3. The relation to oneself

Keeping silent helps us to instruct, liberate, keep in balance, and heal ourselves. It is our responsibility to stop and rest.

Respecting one's vital space and recharging oneself to better give are maxims that are productive of energy! Caregivers absolutely need a time to rest so as to be able to draw out of themselves all the resources needed in accompanying seniors who have lost their autonomy.

As caregivers, we have to replenish our provisions of mental, emotional, physical, and spiritual health.

The walls erected by exhaustion, powerlessness, the status quo, distress, and indifference that are so often present in the workplace threaten our vitality.

How many times have I seen and touched the high wall created by Alzheimer's, which I call Alzhei-murus! And I am not the only one!

When injustice and sorrow take over the space, the danger of imprisoning ourselves in useless agitation continually lies in wait.

One solution is to stop and rest so that we can better recover our sources and values and, finally, rediscover ourselves. A new dynamism then leads us to re-clothe with tenderness and dignity the loneliness and fear of those who have become "voiceless" through illness or age.

Let us take the time to receive from the cosmos the nourishing elements with which it is teeming; let us know how to name them, welcome them, and write them on our calendars as special treats to be renewed. This is essential. Perhaps we could also share some of them with the people whom we are accompanying: for example, an outing in nature, calming music, a fruit tea, a flower, or a reassuring hand. Don't the residents of homes live in an environment that has been to often neglected by a society that cares little about the depths of beings ? Our compassionate actions are rainbows that the isolated residents need.

Our times of rest can also serve for taking care of ourselves and to better protect those who count on us. As compassionate caregivers, we are witnesses of daily suffering. Our being has a right to its moments of convalescence, however short they may be, outside our field of action.

The philosophy underlying the Congruent Compassionate Approach requires of us an appointment with quiet. Let us take the time to note down when we have these appointments with quiet. Listing the things that give us rest liberates us and nourishes us in a holistic manner.

Within the caregiving model used by the Congruent Compassionate Approach, we suggest to the directors of extended-care centres that they provide on site opportunities for moments of tranquillity for all their staff:

– by creating a caregiving environment that promotes the expression of unconditional love between resident and caregiver;

– by allotting at least ten minutes of solitary time, and preferably in a place that is conducive to quiet and relaxation, so that staff members can leave behind them their preoccupations before returning to their work;

– by inviting them to practise self-emptying so that the energy necessary to accompany the residence's clientele can emerge.

This time of rest and complete silence can give strength to those who have chosen the realm of health care as a place to actualize their gift.

It is also worthwhile to provide moments of respite to people who are accompanying a spouse or relative at home. For many of them, exhaustion and depression are all too real. One wife said to me, "My husband's condition is always being asked after, but never my own."

My mother, like thousands of others, unremittingly devoted herself to looking after my father day and night only to find out that Alzheimer's was more and more a high wall (Alzhei-murus), a wall of silence, isolation, and exhaustion.

It is important to listen to these non-professional home caregivers who give of themselves without taking into account the cost, and often without relief or appreciation for what the are doing.

Because the relation to one's self can lead to the healing of ourselves, I dedicate one of my poems to the caregivers who rely on our support and who would like a period of respite. I have taken a number of words to describe the spectacle I witnessed during my time at the lake. Nature can truly cradle and rock the heart that is seeking rest and gentleness.

Path for exploration:

I am going to describe how I take care of myself.

It is wise to take time to empty ourselves
in order the better to fill ourselves again.

Dragonfly

Finally, the quiet of a landscape
replaces my cluttered sitting room,
looking for peace and beauty!
A completely blue dragonfly settles on my page,
exhibiting the colours of her regal gown
like a queen of the summer.

The wind ruffles the waves and
gently rocks for hours
the ducks and their ducklings.
The birds are inventing all the languages
to liberate their happiness
at having full nests.

Heaven is painting itself with clouds,
like an artist who lets her heart speak,
to draw inventively gliding masterpieces.
My eyes enjoy baptizing these images
in a dance of the imaginary.
How good, says the rested body,
are all these moments of repose
when my thirsty life can refresh itself
by drinking in the beautiful.

4. *The relation to the Transcendent*

A visiting philosopher friend deeply involved in developmental studies shared with me his vision of the Transcendent. Accustomed to respecting all the great religions, he stressed the beauty of the ancient spiritual wisdom of Christianity, Buddhism, Islam, Judaism, etc. They all have as their goal humanization; that is, they want to promote the flourishing of the human person in relation with the Transcendent. Furthermore, all the great religions adopt compassion as a fundamental value.

Scientists are in the process of supporting what individuals throughout the ages have felt: the intuition of the Transcendent. Each of us can have an experience of the Transcendent and feel called to cast ourselves resolutely into realizing an infinite project.

Some people refer to this same cosmic verity by various names: God, Presence, Life Principle, Ultimate Power, etc. Our need for interiority compels us to find a guide capable of directing the evolution of our thought.

Our search for harmony, health, prosperity, and deep relationships discovers interesting answers in numerous philosophies and holistic techniques.

As I stated earlier, my experience of accompanying a sick friend led me to the discovery of an unsuspected depth. Our silent communication was indwelt by Transcendence. A peace emanated from her. The looks that we exchanged revealed, beyond words, a communion between two people involved together in an infinite project. I was certain that I was showing her a tenderness nurtured by one "greater than I." Her calm glance and her hand clasping mine conveyed a similar message to me. This kind of connection, which is so deep and full of gentleness, is difficult to define. Only a very moving silence can bear witness to this Passion of Loving.

Opening ourselves to Transcendence enables us to enter into a relationship that illuminates the meaning of life. Occasionally, even the experience of a sorrowful event can become a precious gift.

While respecting the name that each person gives to the Transcendent, I confess that mine comes from Christianity. My acts are attached to the very acts of Christ. Paying attention to Maria, John, or whomever, is paying attention to this friend. "Just as you did it to one of the least of these who are members of my family, you did it to me" (Matthew 25:40).

Together, we are givers and receivers.

The relation to the Transcendent opens unsuspected avenues of beauty at the heart of suffering. These moments experienced in full openness to Transcendence enable us to live consolation in depth and intense spirituality in the midst of meaninglessness and sorrow.

Beyond Words

Do you remember the first time
we met?
Like a great lady
of great goodness
like the staff of life,
you spied me out.
Being twice your age,
I was gratified
that you were inspired by me
to become yourself.
Over the years,
friendship allowed us to grow
together.
You received my confidences,
the tale of my wounds
but also of my daring
to tread unbeaten paths.
A career woman,
with lots of responsibilities.
The answer was to love.
We had in common
the freedom to invent
and to risk.
You wept at my pains
and I at yours.
You made me laugh out loud
and I taught you to have
self-confidence.

How often
was heaven thanked
for the gift of our friendship.
That was the first time round!
Today we love for the
second time.
I am losing the memory
and the words to say it.
But I can still feel that you
see me
as a great lady
of great goodness
like the staff of life.
Being twice your age,
I feel comforted
that you are receiving
what I still have to give,
a gentle glance,
a hand on your cheek.
Here, at the Home, my name
is seldom called.
For the most part, I am no one.
They wake me up, feed me, quickly,
and park me.
"Be nice," they tell me
when I dared to say no.
In my file, I am called aggressive,
but it does not say with whom
or why.
Then suddenly, you are on the scene
Like love replacing the law.

Loneliness and fear
vanish in your gentleness.
You recognize again in me
The great lady
of great goodness
like the staff of life.
I need to be loved and recognized.
Does a person have this right
when she has lost everything?
You surround me with love
and gently calm me.
You know how to be there
all the way
and I can feel it, knowing
you often cry.
But beyond all the storms,
You and I deeply know
within
that loving to the core
surpasses all the words
and is the greatest gift.

I have only the deepest and greatest reverence for
Maria, who by her life and illness opened me to life,
Transcendence, the Passion of Loving, and the Congruent
Compassionate Approach.

Path for exploration:

Have I had an experience of the Transcendent? How would I describe it?

5. *The relation to life*

According to the thinkers of ancient Greece, life was made up of four elements: fire, air, water, and earth.

In order to live more fully, we need to depend on the quality of these elements. Everything lives with, and nothing survives without a constant, intelligent respect for these elements. Our days habitually pass in anxiety that gives rise to war (fire), pollution (air and water), and contamination (earth). The advocates of peace, green spaces, clean air, and healthy food are our leaders in hope at the local and global levels.

Within resident/caregiver relationships, these elements drive us to verify our choices in the light of the happiness of each and all.

What is the quality of the life and environment offered to seniors who have lost their autonomy? Do the space and time allotted to each of the residents demonstrate respect and kindliness at, for example, mealtimes and bath and bedtime? What about the meal menus and their presentation, quiet or noise in sleeping areas, attention to the residents' sensitivity to heat or cold, the attentive approach to bed care, assistance given in feeding, clothing, and moving the residents, etc.?

The life-supporting elements are also found in human warmth, a positive atmosphere, and respect for a person's vital space. All that responds to the need that the other has to be welcomed, understood, and loved.

Residents suffering from dementia appreciate that we are there "for them" at meal and personal care times. Contrary to what many people sometimes think, a kind word and a smile accompanying an act do not take any extra time and can "make a difference" to the daily life of the patients. It may be that some residents are incapable of responding or even of letting us know that they understand our message, but they can *feel* the quality of our presence.

Our ability to give with respect and tenderness probably reveals our own self-esteem. The task of improving the quality of life and the environment in a healthcare centre contributes to surrounding the residents and caregivers with this aura of unconditional love.

Life encompasses everything and is found in the infinitely small as much as in the infinitely large. It has been given to us so that we can express the totality of our being and embellish both our exterior and our interior worlds with beauty and joy.

The relation to life impels us to reach out towards the light and to do so in such a way that those who are most vulnerable will benefit from our joy in life. Life flourishes much more when it is shared, either in the service of an individual or of a group.

Path for exploration:

What are my life journeys?

Having lost much, I can still feel.

In the process of exploring and deepening our relationships, we have to better equip ourselves to develop the means of expression of our unconditional love in the healthcare environment. The profession that a person has chosen ought to be the expression of his or her deepest being.

I am going to draw a flower with five petals and I am going to write on the each petal a characteristic that best reflects me.

PART TWO

Different manifestations of
the Congruent Compassionate Approach

The following pages emphasize our responsibility with respect to the persons in loss of autonomy and are intended to awaken our desire to care with a compassionate heart. They suggest some ways that our actions can be brought in line with our words and can bear witness to our unconditional love.

1. Love's exclusive creation

The links that bind us to those with whom we come in contact are unique and special. In their uniqueness and depth, they form a story of relationships, a story of love. The same is true in the relations that exist between resident and caregiver.

When illness or age makes the task of daily living difficult, the quality of the relationship between the resident and the caregiver presents one of the most pressing challenges, but also one that is among the most satisfying. How can we live with, share, and relieve the sorrow of another person if not by surrounding it with an unconditional love that is expressed in healing acts. In his or her uniqueness, the resident can feel the caring act on the body that conceals a whole life's story.

The knowledge and care techniques used in the Congruent Compassionate Approach are doubly beneficial for patients. Only love can get us actively involved in creating and discovering solutions for all kinds of suffering.

Path for exploration:

What are my healing acts?

2. The relation to the other, a story

One of the most demanding challenges is without doubt the experience of loving from day to day. Love alone can trace out, beyond the known and seen, the paths of compassion that I call the Passion of Loving.

The experience of loving and accompanying up to the end a suffering person lays out for the one experiencing it a pathway of compassion that will no longer leave him or her at peace. Like a torment, the caregiver – feels called to relieve the suffering of the other person and to experience the different stages of that person's evolution. "Missioned" by tenderness, the caregiver desires to accompany the patient by helping the patient either to get well or to prepare for death.

The values of respect and dignity are fundamental in building up a secure, empathetic, and calming relationship. In one way or another, each relationship becomes a story of unconditional love.

The cases described throughout this text should be read slowly and in a spirit of openness to the other. An elderly person without autonomy, and suffering from cognitive deficiencies, could be my most precious relation – or, indeed, this person could be me.

Extended-care centres bring together healthcare professionals, most of whom have a real concern for the well-being of the residents. They are participating in a healthcare system whose primary goal is to improve the quality of care.

Even though caregivers try to respond to multiple tasks, it is still unfortunate to see that many elderly people are parked in one place for long periods of time, and that they feel forgotten, neglected, and often physically ill at ease. They go to sleep full of a daily existence lacking in attention and meaningfulness. This reality contaminates both the patient and the caregiver with a deep sadness and even a sense of rebellion. How often do we hear that an elderly person without autonomy has died from a lack of will to live rather than from the consequences of the illness?

This situation, repeated daily, is inhuman and abusive. A solution has to be found.

When the link between resident and caregiver becomes synonymous with immunity to suffering and with power, neglect, abuse, money, bureaucracy, or numbers, it is a strong counter-incentive to pursuing a career in the realm of health care.

Neglect and ill treatment of elderly patients is a scandal denounced by the Charter of Rights and Freedoms.

Our healthcare system is in need of reorganization when it is faced with financial difficulties and challenged with the burden imposed on overworked personnel. New strategies are under study and will become pathways to compassion. Nevertheless, givers of compassionate care are already at work. Their "torment" cannot wait, and their creativity goes before. These are "cutting-edge" men and women committed to unconditional love.

Amidst the efforts being deployed at all levels of responsibility, it is essential to concentrate on the necessity of caring through compassionate actions.

In an environment of anonymity, a senior without autonomy has a face, a story, a heart that beats and feels.

He or she has a name:
Papa... mine, yours;
   Mama... mine, yours;
     Sister, brother,friend, husband, wife... ours.

This senior suffering from cognitive deficiencies belongs to someone's story of love.

It can happen that a resident caused a great deal of suffering to to some members of his or her family. In such a case, it is obviously very difficult for the family to care with unconditional love. Forgiveness then appears as a long and painful road to be travelled. Sometimes, however, reconciliations are possible.

A psychologist once told me that the person whom I saw as having a problem was, instead, experiencing suffering. This pronouncement, coming from a wise person, has remained with me. Forgiveness can thus become the ultimate sign of the Passion of Loving.

I would like to quote here the following powerful words attributed to Pierre Teilhard de Chardin: "The day will come when we, having harnessed space, the winds, the tides, and gravity, will harness the energies of love for the sake of God. And on that day, for the second time in the history of the world, we will have discovered fire."

Path for exploration:

How have I experienced forgiveness?

Each person's story is a sacred place.

3. A listening heart

The Congruent Compassionate Approach calls the caregiver to keep his or her heart open and listening to the daily experiences of the patient.

The gift of compassion urgently calls the caregiver to relieve the suffering of the patient, whether it is physical, emotional, or moral. This desire to relieve suffering survives only if the caregiver keeps his or her eyes focused on the suffering of the patient.

The following example illustrates how an attentive heart can transform a patient who is trying to express his need to be recognized.

> At mealtimes, John kept calling out at regular intervals: "Help!" He was making the other residents seated close to his wheelchair jump.
>
> Each time, the nurse said to him: "John, Sssh!" Without success! Another caregiver tried to find a solution by approaching him gently. He gently asked John if he wanted anything. John kicked his slipper into the middle of the room. The caregiver retrieved it and replaced it on John's foot, all the while gently stroking the foot. John then kicked off his other slipper. The caregiver repeated his action, smiling tenderly. A relationship had been established. John returned the caregiver the most beautiful smile, a smile that had never before been seen on his face. The caregiving team thus discovered that John's calling out was his way of letting everyone know that he existed and that he wanted to exist still for someone. That evening, the caregiver who found out

how to connect with John's deepest desire went home with tears in his eyes. His heart was smitten with the desire to uncode the messages of seniors with cognitive deficiencies.

The Congruent Compassionate Approach had made both resident and the caregiver beneficiaries of an authentic relationship.

A case like that of John opens to us the doors of tenderness, creativity, and challenge. It is not always easy to uncode a situation, to reassure the patient, and to understand the response. The very fact of seeking to do so, however, enriches the quality of life in a care centre. Try to imagine John's joy. That makes the trouble worthwhile.

The Congruent Compassionate Approach reveals to the caregiver his or her mission, namely, to be "a voice" for those voiceless whose groanings are not heard.

I was alone; you stayed by me, with me.
I was uncomfortable; you put a pillow in place for me.
I was trapped in my silence; your hand reassured me.
I was nameless; your eyes told me
I was someone for you.
I was cold; your hand checked the temperature
of my feet.

Path for exploration:

Can I uncode what is not being said by someone with a cognitive deficiency? Can I see the results?

4. When the heart loves "to the core"

The Congruent Compassionate Approach is born out of the "viscera" of the caregiver who perceives and understands suffering from the sensitivity of his or her heart. He or she feels both what is said and what is not said by the other and acts on it. The caregiver's empathetic attitude connects with people in loss of autonomy and brings them a better quality of being. As Antoine de Saint-Exupéry said, "What is essential is invisible to the eyes; only the heart can see it."

The Congruent Compassionate approach is linked to the sacred character of the person being cared for.

In my meetings with caregivers, they have shared with me the enabling experiences for which they are grateful as well as the incalculable amount of suffering created by indifference and false excuses.

One of love's missions is to find viable solutions for the present moment. It is unacceptable, for example, that an elderly person is confined groaning in a wheelchair while waiting for the bathroom. What if I were this person?

We rightly denounce war. To denounce the daily suffering of those people who are dependent upon us is to ensure respect and dignity for them.

It would also be wonderful to inform our colleagues about the successes of those caregivers who look after the elderly ill. This kind of sharing encourages research and enlarges the field of compassionate action.

The physical, psychological, and spiritual suffering of patients is a call for caregivers to the Passion of Loving. The caregiver's own journey has taught him or her the pain that an unhealed wound can cause, the good that can come from an unexpected visit from a friend, and the comfort that can result when a patient is treated with speed, understanding, and expertise.

A senior suffering from dementia belongs to the human race too. For this senior, as for all other humans, little joys like great joys have their place.

I am remembering Marcella, whose smile and goodness did me good as I watched her skilfully manipulating the hydraulic lift over the whirlpool bath. She held the hand of the frail lady with the worried face during this "ascension" over the bathtub. Marcella's reassuring words calmed her fears. Instead of turning her around quickly, Marcella took the time to accustom her to this journey and succeeded in gently reducing her fear of the water. Marcella knew that people with dementia are afraid of water. She also remembered to cover the resident's eyes with a towel when she washed her hair. She rinsed it gently, reassuring her the whole time.

I pointed out Marcella's great gentleness to her and added that her family must feel lucky to live with such a person. It was then that she revealed to me that her husband was an invalid with multiple sclerosis. When she got home she spent all her time attending to him and to the children. In my admiration, I dared to ask her, "Where do you get this patience and goodness from?" She replied quietly, "From my relation with God."

Marcella had just reinforced my desire to help and love. I felt "missioned" with her. She was living out the Congruent

Compassionate Approach at the visceral level. Her gift of compassion exceeded the usual and created around her a contagious atmosphere of tenderness and gentleness.

I thanked God for this woman. The person who was dear to me also received cared from Marcella. There are no words to describe the kind of balm that compassionate caregivers apply to the lives of the ill! They are also a comfort for the sick person's family and friends. Likewise, there are no words to relate the anguish that is felt when a loved one is treated with rudeness by a caregiver whose heart has been deserted by compassion.

The career of attending at the bedside of the ill should only be chosen by those who are smitten with compassion.

Path for exploration:

Is someone dear to me in care? What is the story of my experience of this?

Existing for someone.

5. Emotional intelligence

The Congruent Compassionate Approach is expressed initially in emotional intelligence. Beyond the necessary professional knowledge, the caregiver has to possess this emotional intelligence, which surpasses mere technical matters.

> One morning a lady suffering from dementia refused to go to breakfast. She was occupied with a jigsaw puzzle on the table in her room. A caregiver, however, knew how to attract her attention by showing her some toast. She then followed him to the dining room.

This is an extraordinary example of creativity on the part of the caregiver, who might, like so many others, simply have said, "You won't get any breakfast if...!" Taking care for someone's story of love with so much goodness belongs to the realm of love. This kind of approach gives birth to constructive results, whereas the contrary approach produces bitterness and sadness. Compassion dissolves those "catastrophic reactions" that are mentioned in the dossiers of residents in care. The preceding example gratified the resident and the caregiver with an experience in which both were winners.

Seniors without autonomy are adults, not children. They possess a rich past of journeys made through difficult stages as well as moments of glory that are now hidden beneath the mask of illness.

Our vocation to compassion is holistic. To care for the injured or exhausted body of a resident is to surround with attention everything that makes up that person, especially that which is beyond the visible.

It is extremely important to uncode the needs of the patient who is no longer able to formulate them. From this comes the necessity of "taking the time" to be there for the other. Unconditional love is the name of this "emotional intelligence" that springs out of the Congruent Compassionate Approach. The daily experiences of seniors without autonomy pass through a routine that can be re-clothed in all the colours ingenuity can provide.

At the heart of the daily routine, a meal is a special moment at which many things can be found to promote appetite and a relaxed atmosphere. The meal is appreciated when it has been well prepared and placed on a table that has been made welcoming by the addition of a tablecloth or flowers.

> One Mother's Day, I noticed that tablecloths and flowers had been placed only on the tables at which the autonomous elderly were seated. I was saddened by this and asked why the tables of the people with dementia were bare. I was told that one of them might eat a flower. But not all flowers are noxious. Moreover, most of the patients were immobile in their geriatric wheelchairs and could not reach the table, much less the flowers. It is important to be cautious, but also to create a festive atmosphere for all the residents.

The presence of a caregiver at mealtimes paying *particular* attention to elderly persons and describing the items on the menu they cannot see is a most moving spectacle:

You cover me with a large napkin (not a bib).

You speak to me; I like the words you choose.

I don't have strength anymore; you feed me delicately.

It is difficult for me to swallow; you use a little spoon adapted to my needs.

I can no longer say that the food is hot or cold; you check its temperature.

You wipe my mouth gently with a napkin.

You give me little sips of the drink, giving me time between swallows.

My meal thus becomes a feast at the heart of my silence.

A place where there is compassionate care is a place of life. The Passion of Loving decorates it by making it a place where resident and caregiver are both treated like guests.

Path for exploration:

I am going to describe how I am creative at mealtimes.

A place where there is compassionate care
is a place of life.

6. A personal commitment

The Congruent Compassionate Approach is a personal option, a conscious choice, and a call made to each and every caregiver. The caregiver's career becomes the expression of a gift of compassion that he or she recognizes. This gift of compassion is a pre-requisite for everyone working in health care.

In order to identify one's gift of compassion, it is essential that both the members of the administration and the caregivers live out the following stage required by the Congruent Compassionate Approach: listening to the one's own inner experience.

When the gift of compassion is recognized and shared by the entire team working in an extended-care residence, the mission statement is, in its fullest sense, a mission of compassion. It is expressed in a manner that is dynamic, authentic, and creative. Every person working in health care owes it to him or herself to be a leader in compassion. The suffering of seniors with dementia sets the guidelines for our words and actions. It inspires our decisions in this area in which our healing acts are actualized.

We are healers only if we are there for those seniors with dementia and ready to follow their rhythm, while being careful to respect their stories. It is thus that we are promoters of humanity and builders of a healthcare environment that is harmonious, secure, and a witness to unconditional love.

A healthcare institution needs to pay attention to promoting the holistic dimension of its services. It is the home of the residents for as long as they are there. We are at their service and our timetable has to be adjusted to their needs above all.

Seniors without autonomy appreciate at all times, day or night, an atmosphere that exudes rest, trust, and comfort.

I was tired; you let me rest.

I was sleeping; you woke me gently with a soft light.

I opened my eyes and saw you smile.

I am immobile; you know how to turn me gently.

I don't like being dependent; you revive my dignity.

My silence dictates pride; you dress me tastefully.

My footsteps have become slow; you walk along with me at my pace.

You position my wheelchair so that my fragile bones are spared.

I am suffering from a cognitive disability, and you know that I prefer positive messages to prohibitions and no's.

The day is sunny; you take the time to bring me outside; you know what I want and that I thank you.

Inside or outside, you put me in a pleasant place, the garden of my daily being.

Path for exploration:

*How can I create a "home"
for the residents of a healthcare centre?*

7. The expression of the gift

The understanding of our individual journeys can give birth to the capacity to grow and to become what we dream of being in our deepest selves.

The caregiver's uniqueness is engraved in the gift he or she bears. Just like an artist who picks up his palette at the beginning of his inspiration and signs the painting at the end. One's experience and expertise are closely linked to one's natural talents as expressed in words and actions. What we call "common sense" cannot be learned from books.

The Congruent Compassionate Approach is expressed through a constant preoccupation to answer the needs of vulnerable and dependent people. Good judgement is an innate talent, like intuition and sensitivity. Tact, creativity, diplomacy, and ethics are signs of an ever-attentive sensibility.

Caregivers who are faithful to the ethical principles that guide them, respect those whom they are accompanying and who, like them, have made a journey consisting of ordinary and unique moments.

The quality of the words and acts of the persons who intervenes does not have its source in a job description. While the latter may be necessary, the caregivers are actually moved by their gift to comfort and relieve at the present moment any kind of suffering. In no case, however, should they make those in their charge undergo their own personal difficulties.

Confrontation, humiliation, and neglect of the appeals of the suffering elderly are not acceptable at any time.

Caregivers at the bedside of residents play one of the most important roles in the area of health care. Their huge contribution to watching over and attending to the physical and emotional comfort of the residents deserves to be recognized, encouraged, and professionally respected. This requires an increased exchange at the level of teamwork and the most equitable kind of wage contract.

The authenticity of each caregiver's commitment is revealed in the exercise of decisional powers at all levels of authority.

Path for exploration:

What is my unique manner of being a caregiver?

8. Evaluation of quality of care

An extended-care centre, whether of the family or institutional type, requires the expression of compassionate words and acts on a continuous basis. The mission statement of a care centre is thus lived out visibly and tangibly in the ordinary, day-to-day events. It extends beyond the framed statement decorating the entrance of the residence. The great challenge is to witness to it and to make it more and more contagious as the "living word and concrete action" of congruence and compassion.

From this, each member of staff choosing the Congruent Compassionate Approach in a deep and authentic way can be on the pathway of unconditional love.

Some of the cases mentioned above illustrate the benefits of the compassionate approach in the healthcare milieu. The following is another experience that reveals the dangers in a lowering of vigilance.

A daughter was visiting her mother at mealtime. The mother was seated at table and getting ready to eat. In front of her was an elderly lady with loss of autonomy who was not feeling well and vomited into a small container that had been placed before her on the table. The two female residents were visibly ill at ease. Seated next to her mother, the daughter heard the efforts of the sick lady and looked around for help. The other residents in the dining room and the staff who were helping out did not react in any way, however. A nurse several feet away was busy with administrative matters. Confronted with this situation, the daughter found a place farther away for her mother. The two people without autonomy were thus able to function more freely.

In shock, the visitor approached the nurse to tell her what had happened. The nurse excused herself by saying that after so many years working with residents she had become immune to events like that. The daughter then asked her, "If I joined your family at home for a meal, would you think it all right if I vomited at table?" The nurse, clearly stunned, again excused herself by affirming that the situation would not be repeated.

The following day, the daughter returned to help her mother at mealtime because her mother's paralysis required more than the ten minutes that a caregiver could usually allot to her. A lady regularly employed by the family was also present, and an exchange occurred about what had happened the previous day. In hopes of reassuring the daughter, this lady told her not to worry because her mother probably would not even remember the kind of care she received. (What an inappropriate comment!) Several days later the same situation reoccurred.

This story, which is many times repeated, obviously raises a number of questions. How do we perceive the feelings and emotions of those people over whom we have charge? Do we display neglect or abuse in their regard? Have we become immune, cloaked in a paralysing lack of sensitivity? What about respect and dignity? Ethics? Trust? Supervision? The mission statement? The accreditation of our care centre? Congruence? Responsibility? Our society? A case like that above is not unique. And this list of questions comprises the «torment" of the caregivers and the family and friends of the patient who risk being seen as people who are always criticizing and upsetting the status quo. Still, it is legitimate to express one's worry when confronted with such visibly anomalous situations that care centres have reached the point of not even seeing as such.

Inasmuch as we live in an increasingly aging society, we ought to be ensuring compassionate care for all people with loss of autonomy. Once again, we are responsible for the way in which we treat the elderly ill that we shall one day be...

An extended-care centre must place the emphasis on the quality of care lavished on the residents suffering from cognitive deficiencies. It is only through a model of respectful care firmly anchored in compassion that a residence can be said to be faithful to the Congruent Compassionate Approach. This faithfulness is demonstrated and verified when the Passion of Loving and the gift of compassion comprise the reputation of each caregiver and of the whole group in charge of the residence. Collaboration between everyone creates vigilance, which, in turn, guarantees the brightest kind of care environment.

What more could be said about this care model when it is enhanced by a harmonious décor that creates a pleasant ambiance for everyone! A number of avenues are worth exploring to bring this about. Being a specialist in humanity means that one takes care for the global well- being of each person.

Path for exploration:

What are my criteria for evaluating quality of care?

9. *The need to belong*

Seniors without autonomy have lived through a long narrative with many chapters. They are asking us to help them write a conclusion signed with the gift of compassion. The fear, anxiety, and worry of the person with dementia are perceived, understood, and relieved in this way. Each staff member brings his or her personal touch to making residents feel secure and to surrounding them with calm. Even though injured and with diminished capacities, these residents always retain a side of their personality that makes them attractive.

The Congruent Compassionate Approach promotes the creation of a special connection between the resident and the caregiver. The need for emotional security is especially strong in people who are gradually losing their cognitive capacities and sense of orientation. Seniors with cognitive deficiencies have to mourn the loss of many things: health, freedom, intimacy, home, family, friends, the power to make their own decisions. Only their ability to feel remains – yes, to *feel* – and this is the case at every stage of their illness.

The confusion, fear, and anxiety that these people are experiencing call for care that makes them feel secure and calms them. Creating a sense of security, calming them, and emotionally accompanying these patients are the attitudes that must characterize every intervention by a caregiver.

Elderly people are not children and cannot return to their childhood. Their past is rooted in a family history that they bring with them, even if they do not appear to realize it. They continue to belong to their family. And they need to be granted the same love, attention, and understanding they had before their illness.

Like us, the senior who has lost his or her autonomy needs to feel wanted, loved, and respected unconditionally. It is therefore essential to emphasize the importance of

- not talking about the person's condition in his or her presence, or without including the person, even if the person does not seem to be following the conversation;
- addressing the person with respect in a natural, adult tone of voice;
- letting the person know when his or her wheelchair is going to be moved or personal care administered to him or her;
- talking to the person while feeding or bathing him or her, etc.;
- maintaining the person's degree of independence for as long as possible.

At all times the resident should be the beneficiary of our sense of delicacy and our openness to his or her needs and the narrative that is continuing to be written with us. The connections that have been established between the resident with dementia and the members of his or her family and friends remain of primary importance. One does not uproot an old tree without risk of its dying.

Everyone who is admitted to a residence dwells there but without really belonging to it. While it is possible to make connections in this milieu and even to be happy, only the heart chooses the place of its belonging.

It therefore matters that a caregiving team consist of professional interveners, family members, and close friends of the resident. A daily ambiance of trust and collaboration up to the last moments presents each member of the team with the possibility of writing along with the person who is being cared for and loved the conclusion to a story of love.

Path for exploration:

What do seniors without autonomy feel when they are with me? I am going to describe how I ensure their respect and dignity.

10. A new way

The Congruent Compassionate Approach offers a model of caregiving that wants to reflect greater respect and dignity for patients. It also strengthens existing models that already witness to compassion.

Many factors contribute to building the bridges that will hasten the progress of hope, love, and competence. Crisis situations give rise to questioning that in turn opens onto solutions leading out of the beaten paths.

What is wonderful is that the Passion of Loving creates unexpected encounters with people from different fields of endeavour who are thinking about the same challenge. Many of them can unite with the itinerary of compassionate caregivers. Their hearts beat to the rhythm of their stories of love.

We can journey together and discover the ways in which compassion is incarnated so that its full healing power may burst forth in the universe of each person.

Everyone wants to be respected to the end of the last chapter of his or her life.

The compassionate and loving caregiver is privileged to write along with the senior without autonomy the conclusion of his or her unique adventure, a conclusion faithful to the sacred character of all the chapters preceding it. This conclusion, even under the most fragile of appearances, conceals dimensions filled with strength and beauty. It is a conclusion based on respect and dignity and opens onto a singular life's journey: the creation of a caregiving environment that offers unconditional love to every suffering people!

Path for exploration:

What conclusion would I as a caregiver like to write?

"Missioned" by tenderness,
the caregiver desires to accompany the patient
by helping the patient either to get well
or to prepare serenely for death.

My heart's desire

I would like everyone with the gift of compassion to unite deeply with another person in his or her suffering. It is an incredibly enriching experience.

The call to compassion that we have freely received is able to lessen the torment of the Passion of Loving. This is the gift that I ask the Author of all gifts to give you and me. Using it to become *promoters of humanity* will enable us to write the most beautiful stories of love in our lives.

We are all for one another givers and receivers of care...

I deeply desire that all seniors with loss of autonomy be received and loved with an unconditional love by healthcare professionals at every level.

May the love of caregivers always be greater than the suffering of patients! This is the goal of the Congruent Compassionate Approach.

Have a wonderful journey, and take good care of others – and of yourself!

The Flower of Compassion

Throughout her lengthy illness,
our derarest Maria painted
15 000 flowers
like the one that now forms
the logo of our Centre and that we call
"the flower of compassion."
These thousands of flowers are used to raise funds
for the construction of a model residence
where the Congruent Compassionate Approach
will be lived out in practice.
There, care based on unconditional love
will be offered to seniors with cognitive illnesses.

To participate in this dream, contact us at:
Paré Labrecque Training Centre
Box 12, site 15, RR 1
Sylvan Lake AB
T4S 1X6
compassion@parelabrecque.com
www.parelabrecque.com

Invitation

I would like to invite you to share with us the wealth of your experience. Write to us!

Please visit our Website: www.parelabrecque.com
There you will find information on:

  – the origin of the Paré Labrecque Training Centre and its mission;
  – the special story of our logo (the five petals around a heart);
  – availability of speakers;
  – workshops on the Congruent Compassionate Approach;
  – the identifying and training of leaders of compassion in the Congruent Compassionate Approach in your area;
  – your membership card;
  – gift certificates;
  – the Centre's dream;
  – ways to financially support our mission.[5]

---

[5] The *Paré Labrecque Training Centre* is a non-profit organization authorized to issue income tax receipts.

Testimonies

As the wife of Léo who had Alzheimer's, I would like to thank and encourage all compassionate caregivers. I would also like to express my gratitude to those men and women who are looking after their spouses and for whom the road is often difficult and lonely. As people who are seeking a more compassionate humanity, we are all called to be "givers" in our own ways. May this book be a beacon for each of us.

Georgette Léger-Paré

The hope and wisdom that emanate from the Congruent Compassionate Approach are grounded in an experience that unites all human beings: the fragility and compassion that each person feels when confronted with the suffering of another. The Passion of Loving enables us to hear the cry of the poor and teaches us how to respond adequately to it according to a philosophy of caregiving developed by the author and based on respect and dignity. Ultimately, it is the life force of the universe in all its complexity and interdependence of multiple living elements that is at the heart of the energizing life of the Congruent Compassionate Approach.

Glenn M. Zimmer,
Fort Qu'Appelle, Saskatchewan

The Passion of Loving is not in the first place a method of caregiving. It is rather the fruit of a life that "loves to the core." The author of this little masterpiece, Micheline Paré, is always testing in the depths of her being her "mission" to establish living relationships between patients and caregivers throughout the world. Reading and re-reading this work, as one imbibes a refreshing drink, will help to break down the "high wall" (Alzhei-murus) of indifference to Alzheimer's.

Jeannine Bussières, SP

I hope that The Passion of Loving is widely read so that the comfort of the elderly in our society will be increased, the satisfaction of caregivers will be doubled by love, and the author recompensed for her great compassion for those who are suffering.

Marie-Paule Levaque, SP

Your compassionate approach in accompanying seniors without autonomy reminds us that we are called to be active witnesses of the compassionate God and signs of hope for those who live in suffering and pain. As you know, the word "compassion" comes from the Latin words cum and pati, which taken together mean "to suffer with." Compassion is the ultimate expression of the communion and solidarity by which we are asked to go into places of sorrow and to share the brokenness, fear, confusion, and distress of the people there. To be compassionate is to be weak with the person who is weak, vulnerable with the person who is vulnerable, and powerless with the person who is powerless. Your reflections show us how we can allow the elderly to enter into the heart of our lives and how we can create a space where they can be heard and listened to at the deep level of attentive presence. I wish you great success.

The Rt. Rev. Frederick Henry,
Bishop of Calgary

A person unfolds as a plant flowers and bears fruit. Then comes the more or less long and noticeable decline that affects every human being. Life extinguishes itself little by little, like coals that are burning out. Up to the very last moment, however, there is life. And this life calls out for a loving and competent human relationship. Through the Congruent Compassionate Approach, Micheline Paré wants to arouse in the hearts of those who have the gift the art of caring for and surrounding with unconditional love those who have lost their autonomy.

Gérard Cambron

Micheline Paré employs in her teaching the true sense of the word "compassion." We are truly compassionate to the extent that we are able to identify with and feel deeply the physical, social, and emotional losses experienced by our elders and to recognize the scope of their daily needs. Micheline Paré teaches caregivers how to identify patients' losses and needs so that they will be able to give care in a manner that touches the patients' sadness and alleviates their loneliness. She offers the tools and the necessary expertise to allow caregiving staff to nourish and protect this compassion for seniors without autonomy at every moment of their lives. In her approach, Micheline Paré employs the true meaning of the word "compassion."

Yvonne Spornitz, R.N.

For twenty years, I have been producing documentaries throughout the whole world on the work being accomplished by people who are motivated by compassion. I have rarely seen an individual or an organization as committed to the ill in this regard as is Micheline Paré. This remarkable woman has dedicated her life to helping the "voiceless" who are in need of love and compassion. She heroically defends those who are desperately awaiting compassionate care. The Congruent Compassionate Approach is indispensable to our world.

Rick Castiglione,
Cielo Pictures Inc.

Imprimé au Canada – Printed in Canada